FOREWORD

Here at Young Writers our defining aim is to promote the joys of reading and writing to children and young adults and we are committed to nurturing the creative talents of the next generation. By allowing them to see their own work in print we believe their confidence and love of creative writing will grow.

Out Of This World is our latest fantastic competition, specifically designed to encourage the writing skills of primary school children through the medium of poetry. From the high quality of entries received, it is clear that it really captured the imagination of all involved.

We are proud to present the resulting collection of poems that we are sure will amuse and inspire.

An absorbing insight into the imagination and thoughts of the young, we hope you will agree that this fantastic anthology is one to delight the whole family again and again.

CONTENTS

Ysgol Y Waun, Wrexham

THE POEMS

The Sandcastle

A steady sandcastle on the beach,
with a bunch of sticks on a pile of rocks,
crunching waves scattered the sunlit sand,
as the wind stormed an almighty growl,
silence struck the sea aloud,
people fell with horror in hand,
birds flew as high as they ever, ever could,
houses got crushed straight to the ground,
but why hadn't the sandcastle been knocked down?

Reuben Harley (9)

Our Body

Our body has bones, veins and blood,
Those are three things in our bodies,
They have eyes, ears and mouth,
Those are three things in our bodies,
We have lips, toes and fingers,
Those are three things in our bodies,
There are loads more things in our bodies.
That makes us human.

Rahand Hewa Hewa Braim (8)

Thunderstorm

Swish, swish
Whee, phee
Howl, yowl

Through the noisy town,
Over the frightened sheep,
Into the creaking door,
Wind!

Drip, drop
Splish, splash
Helter, skelter

From the dark heavens,
Onto the tossing oceans,
Across the glistening roofs,
Rain!

Mumble, grumble
Smash, crash
Bang, boom

Over the waving trees,
Around the far-off cities,
Into deafened ears,
Thunderstorm!

Angel Justus (9)

Untitled

I was on my way to school
Then I heard someone fall.
I turned around and I knew
Someone was around.
Then I saw something big and round
And something dragging on the ground.
A bag, or am I going mad?

When I got home
I was straight on the phone
To my mum and dad
But they seemed really sad.
Then I went to bed,
Something was left on my head.
I woke up
And fell out of bed.

Callum Brooks Woollett (10)

My Family

F un and great
A ll should be!
M ums love and dads cuddle
I love them
L ovely
Y ours should be!

Lilly Pemberton (9)

Snow

The snow falls, it falls, it falls everywhere,
Let's get our woollies on and make snowballs,
All you'd love to do is stand and stare,
The snow beautifully decorates the halls.
Playing my favourite game of snowball fight,
Sometimes my silly friends say a loud boo!
I always, always, always get the fright,
I really, really don't know who does it.
But make sure you are wearing your warm kit,
Bring a hat, scarf, gloves, boots, clipboard and a pen
To count up your best friends' scores,
Come on out and make snowmen.
Make sure your small mitts don't get very cold,
But first make sure that you do your boring chores.

Holly Byham (8)

Winter

Winter has the greatest months,
It's time to snuggle up,
With a roaring fire,
Your favourite book,
Hot chocolate in your cup.

Winter has the greatest months,
Outside the snow is falling,
Sledging down a snow-covered hill,
Tumbling to the bottom.

Winter has the greatest months,
December, Jan and Feb,
With Santa, snow and Christmas trees,
It's great, I've heard it said.

Winter has the greatest months,
It's very cold outside,
Lying in my bed at night,
Reading as I close my eyes.

Alice Chrispin (11)

Homework

Homework, homework,
Everything's about homework,
Can't the teachers give me a break?
If you don't bring it in –
No break!

Homework, homework . . .
Today is not my day,
As I've forgotten it again!

Homework, homework,
I really want to see my friends,
However, I have to do my homework instead.

Homework, homework,
Finally I've brought in my homework and it's the last day,
I hope I'll get a prize I pray.

Homework, homework . . .
No more of you today
As it's the holidays where I can go and play!

Kendra Laidley

Magic Underwater

I put on my swimming costume
I went to see the lovely fish
My dog came with me.

I saw a spotty fish and a shark
I heard sharks chomping prey
I smelt chicken nuggets.

I touched a wolf
And I turned into a werewolf
What an amazing day
I want it to happen again.

Harriet Hope Norbury

What Car Do I Like The Best?

Although I love the Lamborghini
because it is like a time machine, only faster,
I also like the ferocious Ford Mustang GT
with its spectacular 435 horse power.
My heart beats fast for the Lotus Elise CR
which can speed up to an amazing 127mph
in only 18.6 seconds.
It beats even faster for the new Porsche Boxter GTS
which I wish to drive at 174mph.
The Subaru attracts me because it is
as fast as a cheetah.
What car do I like the best?
I think it has to be the Lamborghini.

Lucas Mouaraki (8)

Today I Met A Monster

Today I met a monster
He was as mean as can be,
Whenever he saw a person he would snarl at them
With his teeth.
His eyes glowed red,
He had a body of a snail,
Legs of a horse and a long, striped tail.
He lived in a flat at 7 Annual Street.
He loved listening to music with his Dr Dre Beats.
His favourite colour was purple.
He had a pet turtle.
He would hunt using his teeth
That were sharpened over decades
And for breakfast he always had pancakes.

William Sharp (12)

Zac The Big Monster

The big monster Zac, needed a bath
The water was so, so hot.
He needed a bath so, so quickly.
Zac will get so, so smelly if he doesn't have a bath.
Zac will get to a hundred years old and he will die.

Joseph Quayson (8)

Grime

There was once a monster called Grime,
He had a gun called Gooey Gun.
He shot people.

Then they would usually be chasing him,
He would jump into the sewers so they couldn't get him.

They looked everywhere,
Then would find and beat him.

Jay Houton (8)

My Planet

My planet has . . .
Falling fire rocks as red as volcano's lava,
Water flowing as fast as the biggest waterfall,
Houses as small as a box on your table,
People as happy as a mouse with its cheese,
Children playing as happily as children can be,
But the best thing of all about my planet is . . .
That everybody is happy and full of lots of laughter!

Amy Cullip (9)

Candy World

Candyfloss clouds
Chocolate milk river
Candy cane bridge
And chocolate beaver
Minty trees
Marshmallow flowers
Sugar cube stones
And sprinkle showers
Lollipop sun
Juicy rain
Yummy, yummy chocolate
Flavoured or plain
I walk on grass
Munching as I go
On the candy cane bridge
Watching the chocolate flow
I took a trip
Above the clouds
Licking them hungrily
While making yummy sounds
My tummy gets full
But there's so much more
Like the marshmallow bees
And dogs with eyes of four
So I continue licking
The tasty candy cane
Then I sit down and watch
A doggy get tamed
My tummy hurts
And I feel like I'm about to explode
Then I suddenly wake up
And say, 'That was good!'

Lina Boudelaa (9)

Fireworks

Fireworks,
Crazy Catherine wheels,
Sparklers shine,
Fizzy fireworks fizz as they go,
Fizzy fountains spitting out fire,
But let's have a feast before we start!
The jiggling jelly is jiggling with fear,
And sizzling steak sits upon the rack,
Melting marshmallows to go with it well,
The burning bacon that tingles your tongue!
Certainly no rapid rain,
But the wonderful sound of the whispering wind.
The streaming sun has said goodbye,
So let the wonderful display begin!

Kira Lee (9)

Fall

Autumn swings,
Day by day,
Golden crushed leaves lie by.
Gushes of wind comes running past,
As trains and buses rush through.
The leaves float by,
The bees all fly,
A boat on a wonderful stream.
The sun shines bright,
Throughout the day,
Under the seas and sky.

Josh Dear

My Cats

I have some cats, I love them all,
They're all different, big and small.
Dime is fluffy, black and white,
And with Tabbi, he always fights!
Tuxy's shy in case you're rude,
Dom is always waiting for food!
Sylvester, Domino, then Dimebag the Russian Blue,
And Tabbitha the tabby cat, too!
Dime's always sleeping on the sofas and beds,
Resting his fluffy head.
Meanwhile Tabbitha's trying to hide,
In a hiding spot Dime will never find!
All my cats, I love them all,
They like chasing paper balls!

Freyja Hinchliffe (10)
Bewsey Lodge Primary School, Warrington

Kitty Care

Cats have fur, cats are fluffy,
The purr they make is because they're happy,
They have sharp claws which cause scratches,
Some are plain, others have patches.

They all eat soft and slimy fish,
But many drink milk from a saucer or dish,
Some bring back rodents and maybe a rat,
A cat loves affection, strokes and a pat.

So if you're outside on your street,
Maybe you and a cat will meet,
Stroke and pet it if it doesn't run away,
It may like it, then start to play!

Georgia Groves (10)
Bewsey Lodge Primary School, Warrington

The Marvellous Moon

The moon is a moody teenager,
He wants things his own way.
He scatters the stars and shouts
And he stomps in the orbit all day.

The moon is a happy baby girl,
She giggles with delight.
She plays peekaboo with her star friends
And shines throughout the night.

The marvellous moon is wonderful,
There is no river or pond.
It will orbit the Earth every day,
From infinity and beyond.

Eninoma Uwadiae (9)
Boddam School, Peterhead

Sensational Sun And Moon

The moon is like a joyful boy,
Playing around the stars.
He smiles at the sun and Earth
And he always waves at Mars.

The moon is like an angry child,
That moans about the stars,
He glares at other planets
And he folds his angry arms.

The moon is like a sad old lady,
That stares at all the stars.
It looks to the sun for friends
As she also looks at Mars.

Nogosa Uwadiae (9)
Boddam School, Peterhead

The Moon

The moon is a moody teenager,
He slams doors as hard as he can.
He throws things everywhere,
His tempers are horrible, he shouts loudly.

The moon is like a sad old lady,
She is crying because she lost her pet star Louis.
She is also upset because no other stars want to play with her,
The old lady just wants a cup of tea.

The moon is a happy little baby,
She laughs, cries and plays with the stars.
She plays with other planets like Jupiter and Mars,
When she is finished playing with her friends she has a nap
And then goes to bed.

Alex Strachan (9)
Boddam School, Peterhead

The Moon

The moon is a happy young boy,
Jumping along, playing with Mars.
He has a pet star that jumps along with him.
The stars hug him when he is sleepy.

The moon is a moody teenager,
He shouts at the stars and the sun.
He slams the door on Venus and Mars,
And does not care when he gets into trouble.

Aurora Young (9)
Boddam School, Peterhead

The Moon

The moon is like a moody teenager,
Who throws stars and slams doors.
Vandalising houses, robbing shops,
Stealing cars and getting jobs.

The moon is like a happy boy,
He plays with his friends and toys,
And plays board games with his family.
He plays with stars and waves to passing rockets.

Sonny Booth (9)
Boddam School, Peterhead

The Sun And Moon

The sun is like a peach with no stone.
The sun is like an orange with no seed.
The sun is like a cupcake with no icing.
It's like a fireball with no ball.
It's like an apple with no skin.
The sun looks like a giant yellow M&M in the sky.

The moon is like a football with no bounce.
The moon is like a bubble in the sky with no pop.
The moon is like a balloon but doesn't fly.
It's like a door knob with no twist.
It's like a Wagon Wheel with no marshmallow.
The moon is like a pearl with no shine.

Fraser McCallum (9)
Boddam School, Peterhead

The Moon

The moon is a shocked old man,
Because he fell and landed on two feet.
He wobbled as he stood,
Also he needed to sit down with eyes wide open.

The moon is a happy boy,
Because he won a round of marbles,
And while he jeered he won twenty more marbles,
Then he went home and he earned more pocket money.

The moon is an annoyed teenager,
Because his friend didn't show up,
So he moaned and groaned and slammed the door in anger,
And slept.

The moon is a shouty man,
Because he's trying to say hi to his friend fixing the roof.
But his friend did not hear him,
The man kept going until his friend got down from the roof.

Paul Fletcher (11)
Boddam School, Peterhead

Sun And Moon

The sun is like a flame thrower with no trigger.
The sun is like an M&M without the chocolate.
The sun is a football with no air.
The sun is a lamp that won't ever go off.
The sun is like a coin that can't be spent.

The moon is like a Polo with no hole.
The moon is like a golf ball that can't be hit.
The moon is like a pea but white.
The moon is a marble that isn't totally round.

Evan Shannon (10)
Boddam School, Peterhead

The Sun And Moon

The moon is like a bonbon with holes floating in the air.
The moon is a 5p that has been tossed in the sky.
It is like a pizza with pepperoni on the top.
The moon is like a Polo mint without the hole.
The moon is like a Babybel without the shell.
The moon is like a clock that is not clicking.

The sun is like an orange that is peeled.
The sun is like a tennis ball without the racket.
The sun is like a Jaffa Cake with the chocolate nibbled off.
The sun is like a light bulb without the glass.
The sun is like a pizza with topping.
The sun is like a cupcake without the middle.

Jason Fernandes
Boddam School, Peterhead

The Sun And Moon Poem

The sun is like an orange that has been squeezed.
It is a cheese pizza sizzling.
It is a tennis ball getting served.
The sun is a cannonball without the cannon.
It is like a bouncy ball that can't bounce.
It is like a clock without any hands.

The moon is a golf ball in a bunker.
It is like a white plate with leftovers on it.
It is like a bowl of Cheerios without the milk.
It is a well-used sponge football.
It is like an apple without the skin.
It is a Malteser without the chocolate.

Caelan Fancourt (8)
Boddam School, Peterhead

The Moon And Sun

The moon is like a bonbon without the taste.
The moon is like a golf ball without a golf club.
It is a Malteser without the chocolate.
It is a clock without the time.
The moon is like a wheel without the hole.
The moon is like a bowling ball with the colour yellow.

The sun is like a pea without the colour green.
The sun is like a tennis ball without the racket.
It is like a Golden Nugget without a bowl and milk.
It is like a sunflower without the petals.
The sun is like a button but a yellow colour.
The sun is like a flame without the smoke.

Regan Henderson (10)
Boddam School, Peterhead

The Sun And Moon

The moon is like a golf ball without the racket.
The sun is like a pineapple without its leaves.
The moon is like a Malteser without the flavour.
The sun is like a peach without the juice.
The moon is like a cookie without the tasty chocolate.
The sun is like a light bulb but there's more light.

The sun is like a gobstopper without the taste.
The moon is like a stone but bigger.
The sun is like a pizza without the crusts.
The moon is like a plughole without the plug.
The sun is like an orange tossed in the air.
The moon is like a Skittle but it's white.

Jake Christie (10)
Boddam School, Peterhead

The Moon And Sun

The sun is like an orange without the taste.
The sun is like a sunflower without the seeds.
The sun is like a ruby without the shine.
The sun is like Skittles without the taste.
The sun is like a candle without the flame.
The sun is like an eyeball that can't see.

The moon is like a 5p in space.
The moon is like a pebble that has been thrown in the air.
The moon is like a bowling ball with more holes.
The moon is like a gobstopper that you can't suck.
The moon is like a Hobnob that you can't eat.
The moon is like a football that has been used.

Travis Heddle (9)
Boddam School, Peterhead

The Sun And Moon

The sun is like a light bulb with no wire.
The sun is like an apple with peeled skin.
The sun is like a red marble in the sky.
It is like a torn plum from a tree.
The sun looks like an orange.
The sun is like a pizza with sizzling cheese.

The moon is like a Malteser with no chocolate.
The moon is like a Babybel with no wax.
The moon is like a bowling ball with more holes.
The moon is like a 5p tossed in the air.
The moon is like a diamond in the sky.
The moon is a speech bubble with no writing.

Liam Inglis (10)
Boddam School, Peterhead

Snowbell

Snowbell hailed a butterfly,
Fluttering astray.
'Come to me, dear butterfly, slow wandering this way.'

The butterfly beat her wings sometime,
Then on her hand she lay.

Gentle quivering feelers and velvet scalloped wings,
Snowbell saw it all so clear,
Those were such pretty things.

The wings a shade of blue one could never match,
Despite the vivid prettiness,
The butterfly, Snowbell would not catch.

The butterfly stirred its wings,
And beat them in gentle play,
It flew into the air,
And into the day!

Marnie Izatt (10)
Carron Primary School, Falkirk

Spectacular Space

Mercury is marvellous in so many ways,
Venus is always there to help every day,
Earth is where we people live day in and day out,
Mars can always help because he is further south.
Jupiter is full of joy because he has just been married,
Look, Saturn has her ring on because she is so happy,
Uranus is so happy because he's always there,
Neptune is the happiest because he is their mayor,
Space is so awesome, so let the beauty inside you blossom!

Olivia Gardner (10)
Carron Primary School, Falkirk

My School Poem

I love to go to school,
Some people act silly or cool,
I like maths the best,
But after my brain needs a rest,
Gym is fantastic,
Just like my gymnastics.
Playtime is fun,
I play with my friends in the sun,
Language is good,
Lunchtime is better, we get to eat food,
Art is colourful,
Topic is wonderful.

William Miller (10)
Carron Primary School, Falkirk

The Ladybug

I was standing so still
I wondered what it was
I couldn't tell
With wings so red
And black dots all over
It was beautiful
I had never seen anything
Like this before
It seemed to adore me
It soon came to me
It was called a ladybug
How interesting!

Laurel McNaught (10)
Carron Primary School, Falkirk

The Country Toon

A Scottish man played his bagpipes doon in the country toon
and all the folks that I ken were listening to his tunes.

Wee Lily and Papa Joe
danced along together
in the beautiful Scottish weather.

The country toon continued to
enjoy the tunes,
until the next full moon.

Sarah Williamson (10)
Carron Primary School, Falkirk

Flowers

F lowers are gorgeous and very colourful
L ovely grass they are planted on
O ur nature is beautiful
W hat wonderful views
E nglish bluebell
R oses are red
S unflowers are tall and yellow.

Rebecca Reilly (8)
Crookfur Primary School, Glasgow

Your Nightmare

You stood silently in the dark, windy night.
You could feel the air brushing against you.
You were colder
than an ice cube.
You saw a tall dark shadow walking towards you.
You could feel your heart beating
like lightning.
The faster your heartbeat was,
the faster the shadow walked towards you.
The trees made creaking noises
like they were speaking.

Amina Khan (8)
Crookfur Primary School, Glasgow

Flowers

F lowers are pretty
L ilies are nice
O n lovely grass they sit
W ow, what a beautiful view
E nglish bluebells
R oses that are beautiful pink
S ome for me and for you.

Zoha Subtain (9)
Crookfur Primary School, Glasgow

Aliens

A liens are friendly
L augh all the time
I f you ever met them you'd know
E specially the aliens from Mars
N obody has ever seen one
S o I want to be the first to find one.

Maryam Haq (8)
Crookfur Primary School, Glasgow

Season

S is for summer and sun
E is for Easter and eggs
A is for autumn leaves
S is for spring lambs
O is for occasionally getting winter snow
N is for new, a new season has begun.

Beth Allan (9)
Crookfur Primary School, Glasgow

Out Of My Window

Trees blowing in the wind.
Dark shadows moving on the fresh grass.
Purple flowers rising from beneath the soil.
Juicy, ripe strawberries bathing in the sun.
Brown cows munching away at the juicy fresh grass.
Birds flying in the warm sunlight.
Trimmed bushes swaying from side to side.
Dark rain clouds moving closer to the field.

Alice Watts (8)
Freshford CE Primary School, Bath

On The Sea

I can see tipping boats and green sea crashing,
Waves like a humongous monster.
I can hear banging thunder and birds shouting.
I can smell big fish and mackerels.
I can feel slippery rocks, freezing water.
I can taste salty sea water like salty, cheesy chips.

Sam Charlton-Thomson
Freshford CE Primary School, Bath

Candy!

The soft yummy taste
of candy
sliding down your throat.
The delicious taste of
Galaxy, Mars, Polo and Haribo.
The sounds that makes
your mouth water.
All the sweets
that make your teeth rot!
The only thing you need.
Yummy, delicious, awesome.
Everything you would
want or even need!

Bella Hemmings (9)
Freshford CE Primary School, Bath

My Poem

I don't know what my poem should be like?
Should it run up the road, should it ride a bike?
Should it climb a tree, should it swim in the sea?
Should it walk the dog, should it get stuck in a bog?
Should it start at the beginning and go right to the end?
Should it slow down at all the ends?
Should it go round an obstacle course, should it ride a big black horse?
If it gets ill should I take it to the vet, and when it's time for bed I wonder
If it will ride into the sunset?

Biba Tarquini (9)
Freshford CE Primary School, Bath

Dolphins

Dazzling dolphins jump so high.
Dazzling dolphins dive so deep.

Dancing dolphins sparkle like the stars in the night.
Dancing dolphins splash in the clear sea water.

Dazzling dolphins are so cool.
Dazzling dolphins are the coolest animals in the world.

Dancing dolphins glide like turtles in the deep blue sea.
Dancing dolphins chatter like mice in a group.

Dazzling dolphins look like the light blue sea on a summer's day.
Dazzling dolphins are the best animals in the world.

Charlotte Pratt (9)
Freshford CE Primary School, Bath

A Monster Downstairs

I wake up in the middle of the night,
Stepping down the stairs,
Trembling with fright.
I think there is a monster down there.
Stay clear,
I really think the monster is near!

The monster could have a big bulgy eye,
Maybe teeth that are as sharp as a knife,
He could have skin that is crispy and dry.
You know what? Those footprints are as quiet as a louse.
Not moving the carpet, not shaking the house.
So I look a bit closer,

I've got it all wrong . . .
It's not a monster at all, it's only a mouse!

Sunniva Snieckus (8)
Freshford CE Primary School, Bath

My Bro

Car driver
Fish feeder
Veg eater
Meat hater
Fast runner
Keen swimmer
Trick player
Hard worker
Helpful boy
Happy chap
I like my bro!

Jon Forbes (8)
Freshford CE Primary School, Bath

My Alien

My alien is my comfy pet
My alien is light green
My alien is big, bigger than me
My alien has three eyes
My alien has a mouth like a nut
My alien has tiny bear's ears
My alien has a piggy nose
My alien has five belly buttons
My alien likes big chocolate bars like me
My alien has wings like a bumblebee
My alien can fly like a rocket can fly
My alien is my friend because he takes me with him
My alien and I enjoy the night, flying up around the sky.

Kaspar Alt-Reuss (8)
Freshford CE Primary School, Bath

The Painting That Came Alive

I went to the art museum with my class,
I saw a picture framed in brass.
The picture was of a lady dressed in red,
Next I saw a boy lying in bed.
Wait, I think I heard a creak,
It's probably from under my feet.
I looked at the boy once more,
Something was open, it was the door!
The boy wasn't there,
But I did see a bear.
Maybe the bear ate the boy,
No, it is only a toy.
I looked all around the room,
I saw a picture next to the broom.
The picture was of a kitchen,
Then I saw something twitching.
It was probably a mouse,
Then I saw a gingerbread house.
Someone was eating it,
It was the boy!
I saw he was staring up at a toy,
He got the toy and went through the door.
Now there wasn't a gingerbread house anymore!
I walked over to the picture of his bed,
Then I saw him, he looked like he was dead!
Now that this adventure is done,
I can have some more fun!
After the day that the painting came alive!

Tilly Charlton-Thomson (9)
Freshford CE Primary School, Bath

Frog

Frogs swim
Frogs bright
Frogs dim
Frogs up
Frogs down
Frogs fat
Frogs round
Frogs here
Frogs there
Frogs everywhere!
Frogs blue
Frogs red
Frogs who?
Frog said
Frogs strong
Frogs weak
Frogs brown
Frogs pink
Frogs fast
Frogs slow
Frogs yes
Frogs no
Frogs light
Frogs thin . . .
Frog! That's him!

Benjamin Catcheside (8)
Freshford CE Primary School, Bath

The Storm

A storm isn't scary
Why are you afraid?
It really isn't scary
it's just a little rain.
Why are you afraid?
It's just a little noise.
It really isn't scary,
So come on out you boys!
Lightning's just a flash,
It isn't dangerous at all.
Don't be afraid!
The house isn't that tall.
Come on, don't hide under that sack.
Come on guys, it's just black.
OK it might be a bit scary.
But really not that much, Derry.
OK I'm scared.
I admit it now.
Now let's go and forget about it . . .
. . . *How?*

Delilah Johns (9)
Freshford CE Primary School, Bath

I Went On A Journey

I went on a journey to outer space
I went all around the world
China was nice
Japan as well
Next I didn't know where to go
So I decided to go to Vegas
I put on my best party dress
And hit the dance floor
I grooved and grooved as well as winning a thousand pounds
I spent it all on drinks
Next I stopped at Paris and had lots of cheese
I really liked New Zealand with all the lakes and the valleys
Last but not least I went back to France and did some skiing there
But it's true to say there's nowhere like my old home in
Freshford.

Hannah Sneyd (8)
Freshford CE Primary School, Bath

The Storm

Can you hear my voice,
through the storm?
The storm is loud and clear.
Can you hear the storm,
echo through the nation?
It's like everyone's screams put together.
I can't sleep.
It's so *loud.*
It feels like it will last forever.

Ellen Wheeler (8)
Freshford CE Primary School, Bath

My Bike

My bike is amazing
I got it for my birthday
It tears down hills
It is very shiny and blue
My bike is amazing
It is very fast
I really like my bike
My bike is amazing!

Hugh Towner (9)
Freshford CE Primary School, Bath

The Kitten In The Cupboard

The kitten
in the cupboard
is thoughtful
and nice.
She's fluffy
and cute
and she's friends
with the mice.
But one day
I woke up
and something was
wrong.
I looked in
the cupboard
and the kitten was gone!
What if she's at the beach in the sea?
What if she's stuck up a bird tree?
What if she's in the forest?
Guess what!
She is with my dog Boris.

Sahara Purdie (8)
Freshford CE Primary School, Bath

Me And My Monster

Me and my monster met on a tropical island on my birthday
She is good, friendly and kind
Me and my monster go everywhere and she looks like the blue moon
Me and my monster go to Pakistan, Disneyland and Paris
And other wonderful places
We eat ice cream too
Me and my monster come home on a posh jet
I love my monster.

Ayesha Salman (8)
Jubilee Wood Primary School, Milton Keynes

Me And My Monster

She is a pretty monster and cute
No one is ever having her.
Me and my monster
We always have fun on rides
While we are up in the beautiful air.
Me and my monster
Go on adventures to France, America and Disneyland.
Me and my monster
Sometimes have cool ideas like being in a great rock star band.
Me and my monster.

Lagshiga Sithamparanathan (8)
Jubilee Wood Primary School, Milton Keynes

My Monster

My monster
I met my monster in my garden snoring
And I met him when I was going downstairs to get a glass of water

My monster
My monster is naughty, scary, friendly
And finally, he is also good.
When he is really angry he is deadly
Like a deadly killer whale.

My monster
My monster looks spiky, bouncy, deadly,
Suspicious, silky
And when he's really scared he is hyper!

Ashwin Panchalingham (9)
Jubilee Wood Primary School, Milton Keynes

Untitled

My monster is as fluffy as a polar bear wearing a fluffy coat.
My monster can read people's minds and is as smart as Albert Einstein.
Bigfoot was just sitting on the seat in the supermarket,
I asked him, 'Can you help with the shopping?'
There was an Xbox One, a PSC and a bench press!
That's when I figured out he was strong.

Sathuchan Sivakumar (9)
Jubilee Wood Primary School, Milton Keynes

Monster Fun

My monster met me at a factory
My monster is as stinky as a funky monkey
My monster is scary like a shy pie
My monster went to the moon at a zoo
My monster jumped home with a comb
My monster is as fun as gum.

Faizan Ahmad (8)
Jubilee Wood Primary School, Milton Keynes

Roxy!

My pet monster has
A heart harder than a diamond when it comes to protecting me.
My pet monster
Is very kind and loyal.
Me and my pet monster
Went to the moon
But Roxy thought the Sea of Tranquillity was to swim in
So she brought her swimsuit . . .
Me and my pet monster
Met while I was being bullied so Roxy came to save me.
My pet monster is
Marvellous and magnificent.
My monster is
As deadly as a nuclear bomb.

Avizeh Hussain (8)
Jubilee Wood Primary School, Milton Keynes

My Monster

My monster is pointy
My monster is colourful
My monster is funny
My monster is slimy
My monster is soft.

Aaliyah Wright-Smith (8)
Jubilee Wood Primary School, Milton Keynes

Oddie Rules

Me and my monster
Met at the doughnut shop
He was eating doughnuts
I made him stop
The doughnut man said, 'Thank you,'
And that's how we met.

Me and my monster
Got home with my scooter
But before we got home
I got him a sweater.

Me and my monster
Also got roller skates.
I left my scooter
And we rode our skates
With Oddie's marvellous,
Mischievous monster feet!

Mevanur Hamarat (8)
Jubilee Wood Primary School, Milton Keynes

Me And My Monster

Me and my monster have great adventures,
Playing on planets,
Swinging to a star then to another,
All thieves in the land.

Me and my monster
Me and my monster having lots of fun,
Never get tired of adventures,
We will never forget these adventures.

Ali-Qasim Tahir (8)
Jubilee Wood Primary School, Milton Keynes

Milky Way

M agnificent and magical
I magination wanders when you look out at night
L ighting the sky in beautiful colours
K eep on looking, you may see a picture
Y ellow, blue, purple and red

W hat is it in the sky?
A round the solar system
Y es, it's the Milky Way.

Nia Morgan (9)
Llandinam School, Llandinam

Space

S aturn is by Uranus
P op in and out
A ngry aliens
C rusty craters
E very planet seen from afar, beautiful shooting stars.

Kadence Crowther-James (7)
Llandinam School, Llandinam

Planets

P opular planets are sometimes big, bigger than my house, not small like a fig.
L ovely lights swirl around Saturn's light, wonderful rainbow bombs go round the sky of midnight.
A s stars pass by, the moon flashes in the sky.
N ine planets float and bob around, nine planets are not on the ground.
E lectric blue is Neptune's colour, the colour of a dog's collar.
T he planets are oh so bright, you need to see, don't close your eyes at night!

Pixie Moore (9)
Llandinam School, Llandinam

Universe

U nexpected things are about to happen
N ear-death is about to be experienced
I have never seen anything like it
V ery important lifestyles have been changed
E veryone is close to death
R ockets have been sent up to space
S o many people are in danger
E arth is on its last legs, everyone is going to die!

Finlay Price (10)
Llandinam School, Llandinam

Black Hole

B ack home it was safe
L ater on explosions came on contact
A nd everyone was in danger
C alling reinforcements, we are under attack
K illing is our job, to survive is a reward

H ell, that's what this is, living hell
O n the battlefield it is worse
L abour everywhere
E mptiness around us, the war has ended.

Aneirin Parton (10)
Llandinam School, Llandinam

The Solar System

S hivering shooting stars
O range-shaped planets
L anding astronauts
A mazing shiny night
R ainbow explosion

S himmering galaxy
Y et the explosion is so shiny
S uch a shine
T iny, shooting, shiny star
E xcellent rainbow colours
M oon shining on the stars.

Cerwyn Hayes-Gamble (8)
Llandinam School, Llandinam

Solar System

S himmering stars
O range-shaped moons
L ovely solar system
A wesome rings
R ed Mars

S melly bombs
Y ellow sun
S pace-tastic
T eam astronauts
E xtreme man
M ercury's blue.

Paige Owens (8)
Llandinam School, Llandinam

Space Explosions

Big explosions, small explosions, all different kinds.
One explosion, two explosions, so many explosions.
Explosions, explosions, so beautiful.
What colours are they?
Red, blue, white and green.
So many colours, I must say!

Lots and lots of explosions.
How many are there?
A hundred, a thousand or maybe two thousand!
And maybe even more.
Lots of explosions, so many I can't even count.

Holly Hughes (8)
Llandinam School, Llandinam

Space – Haiku

Shining, shimmering
Stars, space. Planets, galaxies,
So very far up.

Brendan Croft (8)
Llandinam School, Llandinam

Sky

The night sky
The moon is in the sky
All bright and white
All shiny and bright
The darkness makes me sad
The moon and stars make me happy.

Anaya Jones (8)
Llandinam School, Llandinam

Solar System

S miling planets
O range-shaped moon
L ovely sun
A stronaut bobbing along
R aising bombs

S miling sun
Y ellow sun
S mall stars
T ravelling stars
E lectric rings
M ercury, blue.

Harriet Jones (9)
Llandinam School, Llandinam

Night Sky

N ow it is dark
I n the sky I can see
G olden stars sparkling
H igh above my head
T he moon looks at me

S leeping I am happy
K nowing they are there
Y o-yo sky at night.

Chloe Pugh (7)
Llandinam School, Llandinam

Planets

P erfect planets racing through the sky
L ovely luxurious lights shining on the moonlight
A star shining near the moon
N ine, but now eight planets in the solar system
E very planet has a name
T rillions of stars are floating in the solar system
S o many planets turning around every second.

Phoebe Davies-Evans
Llandinam School, Llandinam

Stars

Stars are shining
Sun is glimmering
Planets are around me
I am far away from Earth
I want to go and claim a planet
Mars is a planet
I went to it
I saw a man, he claimed it was his
When he went I claimed it
In the name of Earth!

Nuala Parton
Llandinam School, Llandinam

Planets

P lanets are big
L ook up and see
A person went to space
N eptune is a giant planet
E arth is where we live
T itan is a moon
S aturn is light.

Cameron Anderson (6)
Melvich Primary School, Thurso

Neil Armstrong

N eil 1970, Neil set off
E arth was the planet he left
I n Apollo 11
L eaving his rucksack behind

A stronauts put your seatbelts on please
R emember gravity is not strong on the moon
M oon mission has begun
S pace, here I come!
T rying to set a world record
R ace against Russia
O ne giant leap for mankind
N o! I've left my camera in my rucksack
G et me back to Earth!

Louise Findlay (8)
Melvich Primary School, Thurso

Rocket

R ed fire makes the rocket go
O ut into space
C rammed in like sardines
K eep calm and keep your belt on
E xtremely fast
T akes us up to the moon.

Tyler Gunn (6)
Melvich Primary School, Thurso

Rocket

R ocks and shakes
O ut of space
C olourful explosion
K ing of the sky
E arth looks so small
T his is out of this world!

Lewis Mackay (8)
Melvich Primary School, Thurso

Moon

M ade of rock with craters
O ut in space
O n it landed Apollo
N ear Venus in our system.

Dylan Mackay (5)
Melvich Primary School, Thurso

Alien

A strange creature
L iving on different planets
I nvestigating what humans do
E xtremely dangerous
N aughty, nosy, noisy things.

Donnie Sutherland (7)
Melvich Primary School, Thurso

Stars

S o shiny up in space
T iny, pointy shape
A two triangle shape
R acing through the sky all night
S ilver shiny zigzag.

Olivia MacKay (7)
Melvich Primary School, Thurso

Planets In Space

P lanets are big or small
L iving in the solar system are the planets
A ll of us live on Earth
N ASA were the first people on the moon
E arth is where life lives
T he sun is the biggest star in the universe
S tars are what we see at night

I n space is where the planets live
N eil Armstrong was the first man on the moon

S pace is dark but stars shine bright
P eople live on Earth, it's busy
A pollo II was the first spacecraft on the moon
C reatures live on planets, we call them aliens
E xciting new developments in 2020.

Eilidh Sutherland (8)
Melvich Primary School, Thurso

Jupiter

J ust so big
U p in space
P eople don't live there
I t's the biggest planet
T urning all around
E very astronaut wants to get there
R ound the sun it spins.

Kai Dall (6)
Melvich Primary School, Thurso

Autumn

Autumn is a time to spend with your family full of love
Hearing birds singing their morning song gleefully
Golden leaves falling on the ground
Autumn is a time playing on computer games joyfully
With a cup of hot chocolate
Everyone having a nap while watching TV
Golden leaves likes soft precious gold.

Ryan Rowhani (8)
Milecastle Primary School, Newcastle Upon Tyne

Summer

As hot as a fireball hitting me
A great day at the beach
A fun freezing water fight
An ice cream van chiming in the sun
An extraordinary ice cream melting down my chin

As hot as a desert
A great day for a walk
A great ginormous day
The waves splashing in the sun
An awesome piece of chocolate dripping down my chin.

Matthew Spring (8)
Milecastle Primary School, Newcastle Upon Tyne

Spring

Spring is . . .
bunnies as soft as a blanket
hopping in the sun.

Spring is . . .
tiny new buds
growing on the beautiful trees.

Spring is . . .
heavy April showers
splashing in muddy puddles.

Spring is . . .
gentle soft sunshine
warming up your face.

Spring is . . .
time to relax,
that is spring to me.

Emily Duffy (8)
Milecastle Primary School, Newcastle Upon Tyne

Winter

Winter is
like a white soft island
as glamorous as gold.
It's soft, smooth and sparkling.
Snow melts like salty sand falling
through your fingers.
A beautiful ball of icing sugar,
it pitters and patters as it falls from the sky.
My snow suit
is dripping in my boots.

April Nicholson (8)
Milecastle Primary School, Newcastle Upon Tyne

Winter

Winter is . . .
like you are going to freeze
as cold as a winter's night
frantic snowball fights
a winter wonderland
a quilt of soft snow
the snow tip-taps on the roof.
I wish it would stay winter all year.
But it can't.
The snow starts to melt
and spring is coming
my snowman is gone
and no more snowball fights.
Bye cold air, see you soon.
Hello little bunnies, come out to play.

Ethan Waggott (9)
Milecastle Primary School, Newcastle Upon Tyne

Winter

Winter is . . .
A nice warm fire and a cup of tea,
a twinkle of tinsel,
thinking how lucky I am.

The star on top of the tree,
is like a gold, shimmering, dazzling coin.
Silver snowflakes float through the air,
the Christmas tree has so many decorations,
like all of the people in the world,
a red, green and blue tree.

Ellie Shorton (8)
Milecastle Primary School, Newcastle Upon Tyne

At The Beach

As shiny as the sea,
As smooth as the sand,
My fish and chips,
Are all on my hands!

As dazzling as the waves,
As gold as the beach,
My bucket and space,
Are just out of reach!

As swish as the wind,
As wild as me,
My towel is as sandy
As can be!

Maisie Cadwallander (8)
Milecastle Primary School, Newcastle Upon Tyne

Winter

Winter is . . .
Like the Arctic,
As cold as a freezer,
Like the world is a block of ice,
Like puffs of clouds falling from the sky,
I love winter.

Elliott Carter (8)
Milecastle Primary School, Newcastle Upon Tyne

Summer

As hot as a bomb
exploding in the air.
I'm sitting on the beach
enjoying the summer breeze.
Smell the burgers on the barbecue,
I sit outside majestically licking my ice lolly.
Wake up in the morning and sleep in,
the grass is like an emerald glistening at me.
Sunny, soft sand, sitting on the beach,
splash, slip, sing.
We all love ice cream,
smell lovely fish and chips,
and enjoy summer like everyone else,
and go swimming in the sea.

Jessica Shorton (8)
Milecastle Primary School, Newcastle Upon Tyne

Conkers

The
green
hard, spiky
shells fall off the
chestnut tree.
The shell breaks and
inside is a beautiful, smooth conker
as
brown
as
wood.

Alex Watson
Milecastle Primary School, Newcastle Upon Tyne

Woodland Dens

We went to the woods to make one den
Unfortunately we ended up making ten!
So then we went to get some blackberries
Imagine if I had lots of cherries!
We went back to make some more dens up next to a big tree!
When I was walking I fell over and hurt my knee.
When we were halfway there we saw a rainbow
That lifted us with glee.

Kenzie Khaliq (7)
Parkwood Primary School, Keighley

Tasty Hot Chocolate

Sweet, creamy, delicious hot chocolate,
Chocolate steaming in a pot.
It is tasty and brown,
But it stops me getting a frown!
Watery, lovely, yummy,
Hot chocolate in my tummy.
I drink it in the woods,
Over my head is my hood.
The tasty, delicious
Hot chocolate made me vicious.
With the hot chocolate we had some berries,
Imagine if we also had some cherries.

Jasmine Taylor (7)
Parkwood Primary School, Keighley

Autumn

The warm bubbling hot chocolate.
The crispy leaves crunching when you walk.
The wind blowing against the leaves.
The leaves falling off the trees.

Shannon Moran
Parkwood Primary School, Keighley

First Time In The Woods

The woods are really dark because there are a lot of trees.
The woods have huge trees.
In the woods there are lots of large sticks.
There are lots of shiny, beautiful and glittery birds flying.
The sun is hot.
The sun is as shiny as a light.

Lucca Allsworth (7)
Parkwood Primary School, Keighley

Space

S tars glitter in the sky
P lanets with odd biomes
A mazing satellites
C ool spacemen float around
E xciting new galaxies to be found.

Keaton Jackson (10)
Plumpton School, Penrith

Stars Are Always There

S tars are always there
T winkling beautifully
A t the dead of night
R acing around
S tars are always there

S tars are always there
T alking to me, wishing me a good night
A rranging the teddies at the end of my bed
R eading the world a bedtime story
S tars are always there.

Holly Gate (10)
Plumpton School, Penrith

My Favourite Planet

S uper Saturn spins all day long
A steroids are flying round the sky
T hey have lines like a record
U nable to live on
R unning around the scorching sun
N ot the biggest perfect planet.

Annabel Murphy (11)
Plumpton School, Penrith

Planets

Mountainous Mercury,
Vivid Venus,
Exciting Earth,
Magnificent Mars,
Jumpy Jupiter,
Silly Saturn,
Unbelievable Uranus,
Never-ending Neptune,
Pouncing Pluto,
Wonderful planets,
Everywhere.

Hannah Mawson (10)
Plumpton School, Penrith

Stars

They shine like a ruby
Oh so bright in the pitch-black sky
In the middle of the night.

Twinkling like golden sparklers
That have just been lit
At the dead of Bonfire Night.

I think I have written all I know
About stars in the sky.

Aidan Docherty (10)
Plumpton School, Penrith

NASA

NASA
Amazing adventures
Silly scientists
Extraordinary explorers
Always awesome
Rocket launchers
Space launchers
Space stations
Planet discoverers
Finding wicked wonders!

Ruane Staples (10)
Plumpton School, Penrith

Space

S pace is massive
P eaceful and dark
A wesomely delightful
C osmic madness
E xtremely strange.

Richy Dadley (9)
Plumpton School, Penrith

Special Sun

S pecial sun
P eaceful Pluto
A wesome orbiting Earth
C olourful moon
E xploding sun.

Keean Harkness (9)
Plumpton School, Penrith

Stars

S tars are always there glittering.
T here are millions of them in the sky.
A fter lots of years stars will die.
R unning after their friends.
S uper stars light at you as they look down.

Gabriella Jackson (10)
Plumpton School, Penrith

Planets

Muddled up Mercury
Vivid Venus
Exciting Earth
Magnificent Mars
Jumbled up Jupiter
Super Saturn
Unbelievable Uranus
Neat Neptune
Peaceful Pluto.

Megan Atkinson (9)
Plumpton School, Penrith

What I See In Space

S parkly stars
P luto
A stronauts
C olourful Earth
E xciting Earth.

Joel Gardiner (9)
Plumpton School, Penrith

The Deadly Adventure

As spooky and as scary as a ghost
As exciting as an unknown post
As peaceful as the beautiful beach
As confusing as cutting a peach
As horrifying as fire
As petrifying as a vampire.

Olivia Morawska (11)
St Columba's Primary School, Oban

The Amazing Fireworks

As nice as a rainbow
As brill as a colourful bow

As lovely as Spain
As cool as a plane

As loud as a bang
It's like the birds sang

As surprising as a dog bite
As bad as a fight.

James Beaton (11)
St Columba's Primary School, Oban

Fireworks

As colourful as a rainbow
As beautiful as a flower
As ferocious as crashing waves
As wild as a crocodile.

Michael McArthur (9)
St Columba's Primary School, Oban

The Thunderstorm

As deep as the blue sea
As loud as the horns of cars
As horrifying as a ghost
As sparkly as shooting stars.

Justin MacIver (10)
St Columba's Primary School, Oban

Desert Island

As green as grass
As fizzy as a potion
As shiny as glass
As blue as an ocean.

Szymon Chmielecki (11)
St Columba's Primary School, Oban

Desert Island

As gleaming as lights
As amazing as a whale
As tropical as a pineapple
As enchanting as a fairy tale.

Emma MacGregor (10)
St Columba's Primary School, Oban

Desert Island

As tropical as a fruit
As tall as a tree
As shiny as the sun
As blue as the sea

As white as the clouds
As peachy as the sand
As amazing as a lion
As enchanting as Wonderland.

Charles Mwangi Githaiga (10)
St Columba's Primary School, Oban

The Lightning Storm

As sparkly as a star.
As bright as a torch.
As loud as a car.
As cool as a spark.

Courtney Campbell (11)
St Columba's Primary School, Oban

Desert Island

As green as grass
As large as a sperm whale
As white as sand
As cool as a fridge
As beautiful as a tiger
As peaceful as the night
As pretty as a rose
As blue as the sky
As unique as a trophy
As confusing as a maze.

Jamie Wilson (10)
St Columba's Primary School, Oban

The Forest Adventure

As exciting as a roller coaster,
As terrifying as bungee jumping,
As calm as the beach,
As wild as an elephant thumping.

As creepy as a ghost,
As freezing as a winter's night,
As freaky as a haunted house,
As bright as a light.

Eilidh McAulay (10)
St Columba's Primary School, Oban

The Beach

As breathtaking as space
As beautiful as a butterfly
As peaceful as a deserted island
As tropical as fruit juice.

Ryan MacInnes (11)
St Columba's Primary School, Oban

The Fireworks Display

As colourful as a rainbow
As dazzling as a starry night
As shiny as golden sand
As high as a kite.

Shaun Menassa (10)
St Columba's Primary School, Oban

The Lightning Strike

As frightening as a bone
As terrifying as an abandoned dock
As miserable as a loud moan
As magnificent as a peacock

As thundering as thunder
As shocking as electricity
As astonishing as the seventh wonder
As creepy as a lost city.

Michael Wilarski (11)
St Columba's Primary School, Oban

The Peaceful Beach

As eye-dazzling as the sun
On a hot summer's day.
An amazing spectacle like space
Through a telescope.
Tropical like Hawaii in summer.
Calm in all ways
Like the islands of nowhere.
Absolutely amazing like a lion.
As astonishing as a peacock's tail.
As ferocious as thunder.
As deserted as space.

Gordon McGrath (10)
St Columba's Primary School, Oban

The Beach

As beautiful as the sun
As sparkling as the waves
As dazzling as the sun
As breathtaking as space.

Brian Maina (9)
St Columba's Primary School, Oban

Outer Space – Cinquains

Peaceful
Bright sun blazes
The moon shines so brightly
The stars glistening in the sky
Quiet.

Ghastly
Astonishing
Sun shimmers on the world
Mars is closest to the sunshine
So large.

Aimee Bates (9)
St Joseph's Primary School, Clydebank

Quiet – Cinquains

Quiet
So dark and calm
All I can see is stars
The darkness surrounds me slowly
Peaceful

Steamy
So breathtaking
The sun so hot and bright
The sun shimmering on the Earth
Blazing!

Demilee Andrew (9)
St Joseph's Primary School, Clydebank

Moonlight – Cinquains

Moonlight
So bright tonight
So calm and peaceful stars
Extraordinary planets
So bright

Blazing
Sun makes daylight
Earth, my home forever
Glistening stars surround the sun
So hot.

Bethany Christie (9)
St Joseph's Primary School, Clydebank

Space – Cinquains

So calm
Mars is so cool
Today planets were calm
The moon was awesome in the dark
Spaceships

Quiet
Shimmering stars
Moon makes darkness tonight
Aliens, the life on red Mars
Black holes!

Brandon McLaughlin (9)
St Joseph's Primary School, Clydebank

Space – Cinquains

Peaceful
A sparkly moon
Shining stars above me
All of the spaceships we can see
Gorgeous

So calm
Blazing hot sun
The sun is a huge star
Pluto is the smallest planet
Graceful.

Tamanda Gondwe (9)
St Joseph's Primary School, Clydebank

Bright Stars – Cinquains

Bright stars
So dark and calm
All the different planets
Glistening stars and the bright sun
Blazing

Bright moon
Amazing sun
Neptune is beautiful
Earth, so calm and astonishing
Pluto.

Amber McAnally (8)
St Joseph's Primary School, Clydebank

So Calm – Cinquain

So calm
Flying saucers
Shooting bright mega stars
The blazing sun is fantastic
Gorgeous.

Brooke McIlroy (8)
St Joseph's Primary School, Clydebank

Martians – Cinquains

Martians
Other planets
Aliens are creepy
Aliens don't like other life
Black hole

Quiet
Pluto is small
Aliens are evil
Aliens are bad to people
Saturn.

Liam Smith (9)
St Joseph's Primary School, Clydebank

The Great Escape

It was a dark and eerie night,
The moon shone dimly but the stars shone bright,
Through the mist the cat could see,
A dog was running aimlessly,
Oh great, the cat thought,
Scratching the wall to sharpen her claws,
The cat was silent, ready to pounce,
As slick, stealthily quiet as a mouse.
But suddenly the dog heard a creak,
The dog responded, fast on his feet,
The cat screeched as loud as a drum,
Then fell to the ground with a thump,
The dog had cornered her and that was done,
Suddenly she went through the dog's legs,
And ran and ran till her heart was content.

Pia Mullen (10)
St Neot's School, Hook

Out Of This World

Shooting-stars
Mysterious-moon
Strange-fireworks
Dark-world
Cold-air
Strange-people
Funny-voices.

Connie Jones (10)
St Neot's School, Hook

Shining Stars

The stars shine
Like angels in the sky
Planets all around you
Aliens everywhere, dancing
Bumpy surfaces on planets
Darkness all around you
Floating in mid-air
No air out there
It's out of this world.

Max Kitchen (10)
St Neot's School, Hook

Out Of This World

It all started when the sky parted then the alien came,
That's where he was.
He shouted out, 'I'm lost!'
But the echo was buried in the frost.

A girl was wandering,
Frolicking and pondering.
She heard the alien's cry and tried
To figure out, where it came from.

She walked around some bushes and saw the alien.
She was walking up to him.
She asked him if he was lost
Was he really lost?

The alien wept. 'Please,' he said, 'my name is Red.'
'OK,' the girl said, 'I'll tell you the way,
To the left, to the right, then you might get home.'
'Thank you old friend. I'm out of this world.'

Kitty Berry (10)
St Neot's School, Hook

Alien Attack!

Fiesty fellas
Pluto dwellers
Peace loathers
War lovers
Space gun shooters
Animal killers
Dreaded raiders
Planet destroyers
Life changers
Destruction makers
People slayers
Weird believers
Love breakers
Gold stealers
Trick haters
Sword masters
Bow users
Surprise attackers
Because they are
Out of this world!

Thomas Sparshott
St Neot's School, Hook

Out Of This World – Haiku

Far out of this world
I saw an angel flying
Bang! Then he was gone!

Fergus Van Der Flier (10)
St Neot's School, Hook

Destruction

The green sun shines,
As the planets nearly collide,
That huge ball of death,
Thundering towards the Earth,
The first thing was the Astroturf!
The roaring sound was deafening,
Anything could hear it, anything!
As the planet hit our home,
Millions of people began to moan.
Destroying the world like a huge round fist,
As the glorious Earth ceased to exist!

Oscar Mannering-Smith (10)
St Neot's School, Hook

Mr Gigglesworth – The Alien

Egg-hatcher
Children-biter
Not a-giver
Tyre-screecher
Cake-lover
Friend-hater
Wild-creature
Loner-addictor
Human-gobbler
Light-detester
Worm-lover
Cocoa-hater.

Matthew King (10)
St Neot's School, Hook

The Giant Torch Haiku

Giant torch arcs down
Shining from the sun's centre
Shares the light with us.

Charlie Finn (10)
St Neot's School, Hook

Chaos

Fire stirrer
Big exploder
Rock thrower
Tall fella
Lava blurter
Light hogger
High blower
Petrify maker
Room taker
Silent sleeper
Quick killer
Rock crumbler
Ash creator
Slow mover
Tsunami starter
Chaos causer
Building smasher
Hurricane brewer
Life taker
Fire spreader.

Archie Miller (10)
St Neot's School, Hook

Out Of This World

She travelled from gear to gear,
Zooming through the atmosphere.
Her eyes went fuzzy,
A bright light was looming,
A luminous coloured ring with colours galore.

She tried to swerve round it
But it pulled her in closer,
She had passed through it,
When she'd gone through it
She could do anything,
She was out of this world!

Savannah Johnson (10)
St Neot's School, Hook

Moon Mission

The rocket smashed through the Earth's upper atmosphere
Faster than a speeding light year
The man really did not die
But he let out a rather eccentric cry
The rocket crashed into the moon
A computerised voice boomed through the room
'We are here!'
He catapulted himself out of the rocket . . .
And fell into a crater.

The man warily opened his eyes
He looked around and saw lots of little mites
Thousands of little aliens
It was out of this world
He scrambled up out of the crater
The aliens waved goodbye in a peculiar nature.

Owen Pugh (10)
St Neot's School, Hook

Out Of This World

It is a crisp winter morning,
I hear the sweet robins calling,
Icicles sit on the window ledge,
As they sweat and sweat.

The snow falls so lightly,
The wind whistles so slightly,
Baby animals snuggle together,
And I wish this season would stay here forever.

The dazzling snow clouds,
Float round and round,
Drips of snow drop off the tree,
This winter is so beautiful, it's all I'll ever need.

I watch the snowflakes whirl and curl,
And I know this winter is out of this world.

Sophie Grant (10)
St Neot's School, Hook

Pets

Bunnies hop all over the place
Tortoises never win the race
Dogs, dogs can be big
Dogs, dogs can be small
Meow, meow is the noise cats make
Fishes, fishes are caught from the lake
Hiss, hiss, what was that? A snake?
Hamsters and guinea pigs look the same
They always want to play a game
Pets are lovely, pets are cute
I really love them so, so much
I wish I could own them
How about you?

Maddie Trueman-Wray
Throston Primary School, Hartlepool

Water Over The Ocean

Water over the ocean
Moves to and fro
Salty sea, is the life for me
Away across the shore.

Water over the ocean
Crashes against the bay
Stormy sea, is the life for me
Away across the shore.

Water over the ocean
Glistens in the sun
Silver sea, is the life for me
Away across the shore.

Water over the ocean
Searches through the caves
Secret sea, is the life for me
Away across the shore.

Water over the ocean
Sailors cast away
Smugglers' sea, is the life for me
Away across the shore.

Water over the ocean
Circles round the globe
Endless sea, is the life for me
Away across the shore.

Katie Pattison (9)
Throston Primary School, Hartlepool

The Sun

The sun, the sun, so big and so bold
The sun, the sun, so hot and so gold
The sun, the sun, it protects us from the cold
The sun, the sun, still so hot and so bold
The sun, the sun, it shines down on Earth
The sun, the sun, gave us our birth.

Will Tighe (8)
Throston Primary School, Hartlepool

Best Friends

Best friends are always there for you
Best friends can always take care of you
Best friends can go to your house
Best friends can make up games with you
Best friends can be a bit funny
Best friends can be a bit funky
Best friends, oh best friends are the best
Best friends can also beat the rest
Best friends are always there for you
Best friends can always take care of you.

Macey Fleetham-Reid (8)
Throston Primary School, Hartlepool

The Life Of A Football

Kicked,
Spun,
Threw,
Bounced,
This is the life of a football.

Hit,
Twirled,
Pitched,
Ricochet,
This is the life of a football.

Booted,
Curled,
Passed,
Slid,
This is the life of a football.

Used and used,
Never rest,
All over,
Not the best,
This is the life of a football.

Ben Mills
Throston Primary School, Hartlepool

Animal Poem

Snakes, oh snakes
They slither all over the ground,
Frogs and toads
All jump around,
Bird, oh birds
All fly about,
Pigs, oh pigs
Have big snouts,
Crocodiles, crocodiles
Swim, swim, swim,
Sharks, oh sharks
Are very grim,
Trees, oh trees
Are very tall,
Bugs, oh bugs
Are very small,
Chickens, oh chickens
Go cluck, cluck, cluck,
Eagles, oh eagles
Have claws like a hook.

Max Nicholson (9)
Throston Primary School, Hartlepool

A Witch's Potion

Witches make potions, oh potions they make,
Why oh why do they not make us smile with glee?
Witches make potions, oh potions they make,
They sometimes have horrible warts!
Witches make potions, oh potions they make,
They can scare you just by looking at you
With their hideous eyes!
Are you a witch?

Isabel Hodgson (8)
Throston Primary School, Hartlepool

Friendship

Friendship is a rocky ship,
Sometimes it bumps, sometimes it rips,
Some people find a place that's top of the rank,
But some go to walk the plank,
You could get rescues and a new friendship will begin,
But some realise they cannot swim,
Most people don't come off at the stops,
But most do it to avoid the knocks,
Sometimes the ship quickly turns,
If someone sets it off, sometimes it burns.

Friendship is a rocky ship,
Sometimes it bumps, sometimes it rips.

Lucy White (9)
Throston Primary School, Hartlepool

My Best Friend

I really enjoy playing with my best friend,
She helps me if I have anything to mend.
We go to lots of sleepovers,
We always go in the park to look for four-leaf clovers.
She sometimes comes to my house for tea,
I go on my computer and she always helps me.
I love going to her house and seeing her dog,
Then we go out and sit on a log.
We go on holiday together,
We will surely be best friends forever!

Tabitha McQuilling (8)
Throston Primary School, Hartlepool

Why Am I A Pawn?

Why am I a pawn?
Why can't I move like the queen?
Why am I a pawn?
Why am I a pawn?
Why does everybody not like me?
Why am I a pawn?
Why am I a pawn?
Why do I always get taken first?
Why am I a pawn?
Why am I a pawn?
Why does everybody hunt me?
Why am I a pawn?
Why am I a pawn?
Why don't I move like a rook?
Why am I a pawn?
The only thing about me is when I get to the end
Of the board I am a queen!

Poppy Eve Boyd (8)
Throston Primary School, Hartlepool

Your Teddy Bear

If you're feeling blue,
All you need to do
Is trust in your teddy bear,
They are always safe,
Tell them your 'dos' and 'don'ts',
Your likes and dislikes,
Never feel scared to trust in your teddy bear,
No matter how old,
Always have them next to you,
You always need your teddy bear,
Pick me up and take me on all your adventures,
Take me everywhere you go,
Take me to your room,
Take me to your bed,
You can give me lots of hugs,
Scares, scares you might have lots,
Just give me a hug and you'll be fine.
Would you be a teddy bear?

Emily-Kate Brown (8)
Throston Primary School, Hartlepool

My Favourite Sports

Shouting from the terraces
Fouling in the box
Crossing from the sidelines
Ref blows his whistle lots.

Arms are straight, toes are pointed
Bouncing up and down
Spinning, flying through the air
Far above the ground.

Rackets hit, the ball is bouncing
Heading for the net
The serve is good it skims over
But phew it is a let.

The ice is slippy, white and cold
The blades are sharp and fast
People spinning having fun
As I go whizzing past.

Water splashing everywhere
People diving in
Frontcrawl, backstroke, butterfly
As they try to win.

Benjy Millward (9)
Throston Primary School, Hartlepool

Pencil

Life as a pencil
Isn't the best,
Different to the rest,
In a pot
With a red dot,
I never get chosen.

I sit there day after day,
Month after month,
But then he comes
And turns my life around.

A boy, a sporty guy
Picked me to write with,
I was over the moon,
I couldn't believe it.

I wrote letters, numbers and punctuation,
I couldn't feel better.

I got smaller,
Smaller than the rest,
I had to be recycled,
To be used again for something else.

So that's the life of a pencil.

Max Haughian (10)
Throston Primary School, Hartlepool

Jay

I always feel as special
as the man on the moon
I always try my hardest
and do my best
When I do my hardest
I get a reward
I do swimming, football,
dancing
Swimming I try
Swimming so hard
Swim, swim, swim
ballroom dancing.
Spin, turn, hover, cross, chasse,
golden trophies in Blackpool winter.
Gardens
Football, football
Opposition tackle
Opposition injured
Sent off, red card.

Jay Nicholson
Throston Primary School, Hartlepool

Dentist

I am a dentist,
I fix teeth,
I take care of Croc's old teeth.

Croc came in one day and said,
'My teeth are really dirty, please Mr Dentist help me.'

He had mouldy old beef stuck between his 300 canines,
It was a hard job but I finished.

I finished and said,
'Don't forget to brush and floss.'
And from that day on Croc's teeth have been like shiny gloss.

Brynn Fothergill
Throston Primary School, Hartlepool

Alien's View Of The World

I taste apple wood sorrel
And I touch the smooth beech leaves.
I like the sight of the bright red berries.
The talking people sounds strange
And the smell of the buttery dandelions is great.

Angus Trevelyan (8)
Tomnacross Primary School, Kiltarlity

My Poem

I smell delightful flowers
Blooming with bees buzzing around.
I touch incredible grass growing
With caterpillars nibbling.
I see amazing trees growing
With beautiful leaves.
I hear lovely birds singing
With sweet voices.
I taste tasty food inside
But not outside – but seriously, don't!

Finlay Embleton (8)
Tomnacross Primary School, Kiltarlity

Out Of This World

I smell the beautiful enjoyable flowers
And the horrible bins nearby.
I touch the horrible spiky bushes
And the bumpy shelter.
I taste the long spiky grass
And the awful tree.
I see the birds flying high
And boys playing football.
I hear big school
And the girls and boys playing football.

Katie MacKinnon (8)
Tomnacross Primary School, Kiltarlity

Out Of This World

I taste the bubblegum.
I hear cars.
I see people.
I smell some grass.
I touch a spiky tyre.

Struan Taylor (7)
Tomnacross Primary School, Kiltarlity

Out Of This World

I smell very nice flowers.
I touch soft grass.
I taste metal, yuck!
I see red berries.
I hear people talking.

Abbey Sanderson (7)
Tomnacross Primary School, Kiltarlity

Out Of This World

I smell crisps and people.
I touch the wall in games.
I taste strawberry and yoghurt.
I see people playing helicopter.
I hear, 'Yes, goal!'

Torin Peacock (8)
Tomnacross Primary School, Kiltarlity

Out Of This World

I smell grass cutters.
I touch people and spiky trees.
I taste yucky cake.
I see monsters, they are scary.

Ben Strang (7)
Tomnacross Primary School, Kiltarlity

Out Of This World

I smell grass, it smells like flowers.
I touch a jaggy tree.
I taste tin, yummy.
I see a blue car.
I hear men running.

Lewis Campbell (7)
Tomnacross Primary School, Kiltarlity

Out Of This World

I smell the bin, it smells pooey!
I touch the soft green grass.
I taste the bumpy shelter, it tastes yucky!
I hear birds singing.
I see the school playground.

Grace Mulvey-Mackay (7)
Tomnacross Primary School, Kiltarlity

Out Of This World

I hear the beautiful singing birds.
I touch the smooth football goals.
I taste the buttercups.
I smell the disgusting sand.
I see the people playing football.

Dan Waddington (8)
Tomnacross Primary School, Kiltarlity

Wishing On Stars

W onderful wishes
I n the well
S hooting stars whizzing by
H appy thoughts
I n the sky
N ever tell your wish
G ood things could happen.

O n the day your wish comes through
N ever doubt your wish coming true

S ecrets are safe
T o hold in the stars
A ll kept tight
R eady for a time to
S hine out of your heart.

Honor Whiteley
Wellesley House School, Broadstairs

Football

F ancy skills
O n the pitch
O h what a goal
T he ball is in
B ack to the centre
A ll over again
L et's have another one
L et it go in.

Cyrus Moreland (10)
Wellesley House School, Broadstairs

Rugby

R unning fast down the pitch ball tucked
U nder arm
'G o, go,' shouts the crowd
B ravely avoiding tackles
Tr Y.

Tom Dunbar Johnson (10)
Wellesley House School, Broadstairs

What She Did

What she did
Was very awful
It made me feel quite ill
I was shocked, I was stopped
I still feel queasy still.

What she did
Was very, very awful
It made Tammy feel ill,
It made the rest of her gang feel dreadful
I can remember it still.

Abigail Jones (10)
Wellesley House School, Broadstairs

Rugby

R unning quicker, going all the way
U tter amazement from the crowd
G etting faster by the second
B attering anyone in his path
Y elling coming from every direction!

Ben Falcon (10)
Wellesley House School, Broadstairs

My First Day Of School

My first day of school wasn't good
As I carried my bag and just stood
And I walked quite a long way
About three miles to school every day
As I walked into school very, very shy
I looked as if I was about to cry
I didn't look very good or even attended

As I walked into my class everybody looked at me
And wondered what was wrong with me
And as I walked a few steps the teacher let me in
And sat down at my desk with a grin.

Then the teacher told me to go to the front of the class
But when I came up to the class I told them the forecast
She said she didn't want the weather forecast
She wanted me to explain me to the class
But in the middle of talking the bell rang and it was time for break
And I said to myself, 'For goodness sake!'
But on the way outside there was a thug
He caught my coat and gave it a tug.

Tom Nielson (9)
Wellesley House School, Broadstairs

The Rabbit

One day a rabbit was hopping along
Singing his favourite song.
In the wood he saw a fox
That was wearing a pair of Crocs.

The rabbit jumped in a hole
In the hole he saw a mole.
The mole ran away
Not wanting to stay.

He heard a sound that was bound to be the fox.
It was starting to dig with his Crocs
The rabbit hopped out and kicked the fox
And ran as fast as he could from the fox in the Crocs.

Gabriel Barlow (9)
Wellesley House School, Broadstairs

Monkey World Mayhem

A monkey stranded on an island sitting on a pile of sand.
He wanted to set sail for Thailand.
He got some wood from a coconut tree,
And glued it together with some sticky pee.
He built a sail from a banana leaf,
Attached it to the boat with some grief.
He set sail for Thailand but ended up in Australia,
This meant that he was a very big failure.

He set sail again and again but kept
Meeting strange new men.
He set sail for one last time
To find some of his own kind.
When he got there and saw their culture he was so happy
But when he stepped on the land he got eaten by a vulture.

Jacob Sebastian (9)
Wellesley House School, Broadstairs

The Haunted House

When I go to sleep late at night I always see something move,
It pops out of my wardrobe and goes into my mum's room.
A few minutes later I hear my mum scream,
I go to see what's happened to see Mum floating by the roof beams.
So I say, 'Come on Mum, get down from there.
I need to go to school soon. Come on ghost, leave me alone.'
So I push it into my wardrobe and say,
'Stay there until I get home.'

Minnie Dunbar Johnson & Milly Moore (9)
Wellesley House School, Broadstairs

The Leprechaun Bandit

There once was a leprechaun bandit
Who stole all the gold from King Tom
He climbed up the walls of the castle
And inside he planted a bomb.

He would light a match and run out
And waited for it to go bang
He would run as fast as he could
And swore with some slang.

The bomb went boom and the castle
Blew up into pieces and out came the gold
Coming like raindrops
He run back as fast as he could
And dived on top of the gold.

And then said, 'This gold is too old,'
And then a guard spotted him
And went and then he told,
The bandit went to jail.

Pelumi Adeyinka (9)
Wellesley House School, Broadstairs

My Band

I want to be in a band.
I will play on top of the land.
I will play on top of the sea, yippee.
I will play the wamawamaweetippee.
The wamawamaweetippee makes an ugly polpoli that sounds like a kiri kiri

One day I walked across the sand where I saw a little band.
I said, 'Oh no, you're doing it wrong, you're doing it terribly wrong
It's supposed to sound like kiri kiri and polpoli.
Or is it supposed to sound like polipolipapatee.
Never mind I'll stay with polpoli.

Augustus Jackson (9)
Wellesley House School, Broadstairs

My Dog

My dog always made me happy when I was sad,
Jumping around the living room my dog was always mad.
When I came back from school my dog would be begging for food,
My dog was always happy and never in a mood.
When I walked around my house he always followed me,
When I got my dog he was only three.
When I had a ball in my hand my dog would beg to play,
My dog was born in May.

Miyah Woolaghan (9)
Wellesley House School, Broadstairs

Dog

My dog has dirty paws
He cut himself with a saw
And puts mud on the floor

He is funny and fat
And wears a baseball cap
And chases next-door's cats.

Callum Parsons (11)
Wellesley House School, Broadstairs

Please Don't Smoke

Those people who smoke make me wheeze and make me choke.
It makes me rasp like everyone knows.
It makes me feel weird from head to toe.
The smoke they puff goes up my nose.
It hurts my lungs, my chest and gives me woes.

Some people only do it to pose.
I don't think they know it causes any harm
But it sometimes causes the ageing of legs and arms.
But please, please, please don't smoke near or around my nose.
It makes my clothes smell of smoke
And will certainly make all of my family cough, sneeze and choke.
So please, please, please don't smoke.

Samantha Ciclitira (10)
Wellesley House School, Broadstairs

Stars

S ee those dots shining bright.
T o be gazing up in the moonlight.
A s you see all those planets up there shining bright in the air.
R ising up to the moon we set off and our rocket goes boom.

Eleanor Felton
Wellesley House School, Broadstairs

Monsters Vs Wellesley

Running down the wing as fast as wind
Getting quicker by the second
Unstoppable as he goes
As he shoots the goalie dives
Goal! Goal! Goal!

Bowling quick, amazing pace
Wicket by wicket he takes
The monsters don't know how to play
Finally hit a ball but it's caught.

The monsters have a chance but miss the try
He dives off the pitch, now it's Wellesley's turn to go
There is the try, no wonder the monsters are off
Eating pudding pie.

There is lots of noise tonight
We wonder why . . .
The monsters want to stay the night.

Inigo Pullen (10)
Wellesley House School, Broadstairs

The Teacher's Coming

As the teacher leaves the classroom there's running, raging, screaming and roars!
Children jumping on the desks, looking at all the answers for the maths test.
Writing all over the board, throwing rubbish everywhere and slamming all the doors.
But oh no, the teacher is coming!
Quick, get down off the desks, stop looking at all the answers for the maths test.
Don't write on the board, pick up the rubbish,
Neaten the chairs, quick the teacher is coming!
As the teacher comes through the door there is peace and quiet
Every child reading a book, the teacher suspects nothing . . .
They're off the hook!

Silvia Courage
Wellesley House School, Broadstairs

A Moon's Wish

A moon's wish you ought to kiss
Otherwise you'll hear a hiss
At 10pm a shadow will come
Be aware otherwise you'll be a yum yum
You'll feel a tickle then you'll smell a pickle
Up your nose
You'll hear nails cracking and scraping
On your bed
Hands come out to grab and you're gone, you fall
Upon a shooting star, make a moonlight wish
For a moonlight kiss.

Katie Ryeland (10)
Wellesley House School, Broadstairs

Carmen

C ar is very tall
A nd very kind
R oses are like you
M any people love you
E ven me and our family
N unca te enfadas.

Maria Bollain (10)
Wellesley House School, Broadstairs

Blind Man

I saw a blind man, who lived on a sad and lonely street,
He was wearing some boots with holes in them
And you could see his feet.
He was whispering to himself about how he fell,
Into a dark wishing well.

He was walking towards a house
Where there was not even a mouse.
But now for the second time he heard a scream.
There was a ghost in there that looked like steam.

Nandita Gurung (9)
Wellesley House School, Broadstairs

The Man

I saw a blind man in the old and lonely street.
He was wearing boots through which you could see his feet.
He was walking slowly towards the scary old house,
Where nobody has been before not even a mouse.
The man goes in through the door,
There was a dirty floor.
I heard a scream and I was scared,
I sat down on my bed.
I saw the man run away
And I forgot him and started to play.

Carmen Alonso (9)
Wellesley House School, Broadstairs

My Scottish Poem

The loud thunderous rain echoes around the toon,
I cosy up under covers in my bedroom.
I tiptoe downstairs to get shortbread and Irn Bru,
But my mammy had all of it, whit will I do?
I go out tae the shops along the wet cobblestone path,
Tae see a Scottie dog with owner wearin' a Scottie hat.
The strong salty smell as I walk along the splash,
I forgot my purse! I need to trudge all the way back.
I hurl into the house and there's a smell of shortbread being baked in my mammy's kitchen,
There's more Irn Bru, the small bubbles pop on my face as I slowly open the bottle.
I'm cosy and I definitely love it,
My home is Scotland, yeh can't get above it.

Ellie Wood (10)
Whinhill Primary School, Greenock

Scottish Poem

The tartan kilts and sporrans we see,
The Loch Ness monster arises from the sea,
The thorny thistles sore to touch,
The tartan patterns, three colours mixed up,
The Scottish bagpipes are music to my ears,
It will make you cry a couple of tears,

Whisky, fudge, tablet, shortbread,
Mammies with their needle and thread,
The bashing waterfall as it splashes,
The loud sound of bagpipes as it clashes,
We watched the bat go up in flames,
The crowd cheers William Wallace's name,

The rain pouring down like a river of tears,
The historic battles I can still hear,
Poor rugged castles still broken up,
The fizzing Irn Bru in my cup,
Irn Bru as sweet as honey,
Slurping it down, oh how lovely.

Dani Adamson (11)
Whinhill Primary School, Greenock

Scottish Poem

Scotland is a wonderful place,
The salty air flows through my face,
All the children play in Loch Ness,
Even though some were being such pests,
Just try not to wake up old Nessie,
Because sometimes he can be quite testy,
In the wilderness trying to find a mythical creature,
That's why Scotland is such a big feature!

Aaron Gault (10)
Whinhill Primary School, Greenock

Things I Love About Scotland

The cows in the highland fields that moo,
The mammies screamin', 'Ach eye the noo!'
The bright screen of the telly as the oldies watch the footie,
'Ach, it's a Scottie dog! It's such a cutie!'
The sound of the waves crashing against the stones,
The taste of Nardini's ice cream cone.
Coming home absolutely soaking,
My friends nagging, 'Ach, a was only jokin'!'
The smell of wet grass as I run through the fields,
Scoffin' a good ol' family meal.
I love all these things so,
All the reason why I call Scotland home.

Leah Carby (11)
Whinhill Primary School, Greenock

Bonny Scotland

All ae' Scottish views,
And all ae' Scottish moos.
Ae' thunder strikes above ae' trees,
Ae' Loch Ness monster sleeps in ae' seas.
I look intae' ae' frightening toon,
Only tae see ae' bright Scottish moon.

As I glance doon ae' rough River Clyde,
Ae' highland dancers prance by my side.
I prance and dance along wie pride,
Ae' highland dancers ask, 'Day ye mind?'
Aw o' a sudden they start a rammy and I'm off screaming, 'Mammy!'

Ae' tangy taste o' Irn Bru,
Whisky, fudge, shortbread too.

My Scotland is a perfect place,
It'll put a smile right on your face.

Karyss Queen (11)
Whinhill Primary School, Greenock

Och I The Noo

S cotland, oh Scotland ye get me through
C old weather or when I'm feeling blue
O ut in the open dew
T he green grassy hills, och I the noo
T he smell of sweet Scottish stew
I feel fizzy inside as the Irn Bru goes doon
S kipping with bagpipes roon the toon
H earing ma mammy singing a bonnie tune.

Emma McGill (10)
Whinhill Primary School, Greenock

Ma Grannie's Hoose

S ugar sweet tablet
C rispy Scotch pie
O aty shortbread
T asty, oh my
L icking my Irn Bru
A mazing food from ma granny's hoose
N ever short of anything to eat or do
D umpling cooking tasty too.

Sianen Carmichael (10)
Whinhill Primary School, Greenock

Scottish Weather

The howling wind punching me in the stomach
as I walk to Stirling Castle,
The thunderous rain running down my window
as I sit next to my candle,
The clouds pouring down like a river of tears,
The fog thick as Scotch broth as I walk along the pier,
My garden turning green to white,
The thunder booming through the night,
The crispy brown leaves rustle as I run through the woods,
The warm summer sun as I dream of Scottish foods.

Danielle Lawrie (11)
Whinhill Primary School, Greenock

My Scotland

The satisfying fizz as I crack open a bottle of Irn Bru,
Whilst ma mammy cooks her stew,
Ma Scottie dug he's running mad,
Pullin' along ma crazy dad,
Our Scottish landscape, it's so green,
We've the biggest hills you've ever seen,
I watch the rain clatter off the roofs,
Can you hear the horse's hooves?
The pollen, it flows through the air,
I skip home with oot a care,
The bagpipes boom at the Highland Games,
I sit at the fire watching the flames,
These are the reasons I'm proud to be Scottish!

Beth Mackay (10)
Whinhill Primary School, Greenock

Scottish

S cotland is famous for its food
C runchy shortbread melting in ma mooth
O ch, the wonderful taste of ma grannie's tablet,
T attie scones are yummy,
T he lovely taste of neeps and tatties with ma haggis,
I rn Bru makes ma tummy go woooo!
S cotch pie, oh how delightfully delicious,
H aggis so scrumptious you can't stop eating!

Calan McCue (11)
Whinhill Primary School, Greenock

My Scotland

Scotland is famous for its Irn Bru,
Everyone loves shortbread too,
Och! Haggis, neeps and tatties.
What makes you so good?
Slice is such a great Scottish food,
Eating tattie scones while watching some telly,
Fudge, oh fudge, yer so tasty in ma belly,
I love the super Scottish pie,
So I ate one while ma team ran by,
Now that's ma Scotland.

David MacPherson (11)
Whinhill Primary School, Greenock

Come To Scotland

Scotland is a magical place,
It will put a lovely smile on your face,
Here we invented Irn Bru,
We also invented shortbread too,

There are so many designs of tartan here,
So if you like shopping well you will cheer.
This year was our Commonwealth Games,
We watched the baton go up in flames,

The Scottish bagpipes are music to my ears,
It might make you cry a couple of tears,
Scotland is famous for its beautiful mountains,
You might even see some incredible fountains,

Nessie is the mystical creature here,
But you should not worry and not fear,
Mount Stuart is a mansion in Rothesay,
But no one there is bossy,
Silence as you listen to the rain,
Whilst you're on a great Scottish train,
All these facts and stories here,
Please come because we are near.

Harry Morton (11)
Whinhill Primary School, Greenock

It's All About Scotland

Shortbread crunching
Irn Bru fizzing
Tablet melting
Dumbarton rock cracking
Haggis steaming
Mince and tatties cookin'
Wind whistling
Bagpipes booming
Loch Ness monster lurking
River Clyde splashing
Pipers piping
Castles crumbling
Robert Burns writing
Tummy rumbling
And that's just
'Some'
Words to describe
Scotland.

Emily Chan (11)
Whinhill Primary School, Greenock

Scotland

I listen to The Proclaimers as families bring in the new year
I take a sip of Irn Bru, I love Scotland. Do you?
The sparkling beverage quenches my thirst
I walk home from school, I think to myself Scotland rules
I can smell tablet in ma mammy's kitchen
As I walk along the splash I hear the waves crash
I can smell the Clyde
It fills me with pride
In Scotland you are never alone, that's why
I call Scotland my home.

Hayley Gallacher (11)
Whinhill Primary School, Greenock

My Scotland

Shortbread, tablet
And our famous fudge
All delicious that makes you go yum!
My mammy's mince and tatties
In my hungry tum

William Wallace
And Robert the Bruce
Fought for our country and you know it
Robert Burns and James Watt
The famous inventor and poet

The rain and the wind
When I'm at the loch
Where the battles took place
It looks so messy
But watch out for that Nessie

Ailee Gray (10)
Whinhill Primary School, Greenock

Scottish Poem

Smell the tablet being made
Coming to see the Highland cows
Open the doors of Aulds to smell the fresh baked cakes
Looking at the sight of the Highland
After dark on the chilling nights
Nessie the Scottish legend
Daring to go near Loch Ness
Listening to the ghosts at Edinburgh Castle
At Loch Lomond hearing the boats going put, put, put
You can be Scottish too!

Kyle McDade (11)
Whinhill Primary School, Greenock

Pen

It sprints to the
End of the page
It's the author
Of the book
It tells the story.

Owain Lamb (10)
Ysgol Y Waun, Wrexham

The Energetic Classroom

The clock waved
its hands at me
with a great big
smile.

The pen scribbled
across the whiteboard
wondering when it would be
the end of the day.

The book jumped
over the table with a
great landing having
the best time of its life.

Sophie Meredith (10)
Ysgol Y Waun, Wrexham

School Day

At the beginning of a morning,
My school opened its eyes
The gates opening its arms,
As children came rushing through.

The door opened its mouth,
Chattering children burst in,
The chairs yawning.

The books jumping,
From desk to desk,
The pen sprinted across the page,
To get to the finish line.

The clock waving its hands,
It's time to go home
It's quarter-past three.

Jodi Kynaston (10)
Ysgol Y Waun, Wrexham

Victorian Classroom

The old wooden door winced for air,
The whip lashed against the child's poor
bottom,
The stool ran away in fear,
The D hat folded himself up into the
cone shape,
The white chalk ran away on thin white legs,
in fear of screeching along the board.

Erin Roberts (10)
Ysgol Y Waun, Wrexham

Peace

A soft, fluffy, plain cloud shook his head proudly,
as the wind blew across him.
He was playing tag with his other
friends, Milly, Tommy and Lilly.

The page swam like the deep,
sparkly blue sea.

The computer plays all night, silently,
softly he goes to sleep.
Twenty minutes later he is
woken up.

Elisabeth Williams (10)
Ysgol Y Waun, Wrexham

The Park

The tree waves his brown wilted arms,
As the cold breeze blows gently,
He shouts hello to the white, soft clouds,
As they pass by.
He waits silently for the smiling sun to come out,
To join the party
The tree was dressed in his green, fluffy wig,

The large bouncy ball
Strolled across the dark green grass.
He ran in the hot, burning sun
Smiling at the giants above.

He swayed happily in the cold chilly breeze,
The grasshopper jumped right past,
Making the grass smile.

The roundabout spun around in a circle,
It was being pushed by the wind whispering
Its name.

Madison Griffiths (10)
Ysgol Y Waun, Wrexham

Midnight Classroom

In his blue suit and policeman's hat,
the pen scurried across the page,
feeling even more exhausted by the second.

Wondering who will read it next,
the book shuffled around trying
to get people's attention.
Opening its mouth to tell a tale,
making a big noise,
quickly closing it, not wanting
to wake up any of the
other books, who slept silently
beside it.

Wanting to shake and flick
everything off it,
the table just sighs,
doing what it is told,
standing there holding everything,
he is a servant.

Bringing light inside,
opening and shutting its mouth,
the window just sits there,
relaxed with his shades on.

Finding out information,
the computer just plays
around all day long,
then suddenly,
softly falling to sleep.
Then in the morning,
waking up,
excited for who will watch
it play.

Amy Hayes (10)
Ysgol Y Waun, Wrexham

The Garden

The grass waves at me from a distance
and slowly walks towards me.
The grass waves to the sunflower
and the sunflower nods back.
The flowers sing a song
like a beautiful harmony.
The rocks play
soil instruments.
The butterflies see the light on them.
The gnomes dance.

Elizabeth Rogers (10)
Ysgol Y Waun, Wrexham

The Classroom

The door jogged its way down the street
taking a sip of water.

The pen ran across
the page while
telling a story.

The pen saw the
finish line and
thought he could
make it.

Owen Jones (10)
Ysgol Y Waun, Wrexham

Camp Nou

The grass sways
its arms in the breeze
as the football flies past.
The ball flies through the air
gliding its long wings.
The net grabs the ball with its arms
as it comes towards its face.
The crossbar lies down straight
to stop the ball from going in.
The ball stood still waiting
for the end of the ninety minutes.

Asa Riley (10)
Ysgol Y Waun, Wrexham

The Classroom

The pen walked across the page
Wondering when the story would end

The clock waved his hands
Waiting till the end of the day

The lights stared across the room
Using all of their energy waiting to be turned off

The book flipped through its pages
To be used through the day

Nathan Lucking (10)
Ysgol Y Waun, Wrexham

The Magic Box

I will put in the box . . .
the tears of a baby crying for the first time,
one of the snakes from Medusa,
the horn of a unicorn.

I will put in the box . . .
the pop of a balloon on a child's birthday,
the Wizard of Oz's hot-air balloon,
an eclipse that lasts for a year.

I will put in the box . . .
the sunset on a summer's night,
a light bulb powered by an electric eel,
the cheer of a crowd in a football pitch.

I will put in the box . . .
a school bell ringing at the end of a school day,
a statue talking nonstop,
a smile from a friend.

My box is made out of gold, silver and lava,
The lid fashioned with the veil of a wedding dress,
Also the hinges are the feathers from a swallow.

In my box I shall fall into another dimension,
where story characters are real . . .

Evie
Ysgol Y Waun, Wrexham

The Classroom

One empty classroom dark at night,
The book opened up his mouth to share his tale;
On turned the light
When the tale finished, the book gave a sigh,
Then he closed his mouth.

The scissors' arms fling out,
He picks up the paper;
Tears it up in two,
The paper whispers back,
'I hate you.'

The chair stands up all day long
He never gets to sit down,
His legs are really stiff;
Never makes a sound
When nobody tucks him in
He will relax.

The stars came out to play,
Never in the light,
They like to dance and sing,
Before they go in they wink
And whisper goodnight.

Yasmin Parkinson (10)
Ysgol Y Waun, Wrexham

A Summer's Day

Wilted trees kneel down
towards the bruised path,
Flowers lose their bright
yellow hats,
as the wind
whistles past them,
slowly dying, the
grass stares silently
waiting for someone
to walk past,
The river cries
freezing cold water,
As the clouds
play hide-and-seek
with the bright sun.

Declan Russell (10)
Ysgol Y Waun, Wrexham

Classroom Olympics

The scissors had a fencing match
in the paper stadium.

The wall timed the pear with his watch
as they ran the 100 lines at the sound of
the staple gun.

The ruler watched the sporty sight
from his royal throne.

Daniel Jones (9)
Ysgol Y Waun, Wrexham

End Of School

The pen walks
across the page
tired in his
dark blue suit.

The rubber runs
across the pencil line
laughing as it
happily rubs out.

The clock waves
its hands as
the hours fly by.
Frowning at
twenty-five past
seven when
children are not
in bed.

The cupboard
opens and
closes its
mouth,
eating books
and equipment that
goes in.

Lily Clarke (9)
Ysgol Y Waun, Wrexham

The Forest

The trees outside whisper,
as they blow softly in the breeze.
'Don't cut us down,'
'Don't cut us down,'
they pleaded,
'We really are needed.'
Along comes the dreaded chainsaw,
baring its spiky teeth.
The sight of it, to the trees,
makes them all
weak.
A crow soars through
the air,
squawking and glaring
at everyone below,
'Hello, I'm a crow.'

Holly Outram (10)
Ysgol Y Waun, Wrexham

Sister Kennings

A cute sobber,
A little cheater,
A real competitor,
An impressive illustrator,
A hard worker,
a shy talker,
A great annoyer.

Sadie Windsor (8)
Ysgol Y Waun, Wrexham

The Empty Clothes Shop

In the empty clothes shop
down the road,

The sewing machine
Chatters in the cold,

When you walk past
you can see its big
teeth going up and down.

A cloth crawls around
with a ragged old
dressing gown following it.

There's green mossy
things on the door,

This is a shop you
have never seen before.

Josie Howard (10)
Ysgol Y Waun, Wrexham

Kennings Cheerleaders Poetry

A leotard dresser,
A heaven flipper,
A stunt flyer,
A pompom owner,
An acrobatic performer.

Lucy Tasker (9)
Ysgol Y Waun, Wrexham

Sweet Shop

The gummy bears roar loudly as they
Roll in the sugar.

The strawberry laces tie themselves together
As they run around the shop with their arms wide open
And the wind in their hair.

The humbugs scuttle around the shop
Looking for green laces.

The cola bottles jump around the room;
They could be bought today.

The bonbons roll around in the sugar,
Bathing in the thick blue sea.

The sour strawberry fizzed with happiness
As it slept in its pot after a long day.

The pear drop cried with pain
As he got crushed as they were closing up the shop.

Lydia Griffiths (10)
Ysgol Y Waun, Wrexham

Hamster Kennings

A cute cuddler,
A food adorer,
A cage dweller,
A tiny biter,
A sawdust sleeper,
A wheel sprinter.

Daisy Morris (8)
Ysgol Y Waun, Wrexham

The Classroom

The clock is ticking loud
Waiting for the day to end
Waiting to smile at ten-past two
Wriggling to try and get off
The dirty wall and escape
Tired of waving its arms any longer.

The pen slowly runs across the whiteboard,
Exhausted from writing
Writing a never-ending story
Its long black hair swaying in the breeze
Thinking, *when is this story going to end?*

The door's mouth creaks open, yawning;
It has been a busy day
Looking into the sparse classroom.

Carys Edwards (10)
Ysgol Y Waun, Wrexham

Nan Kenning

A cake baker,
A dog feeder,
A giggle maker,
A lovely cuddler,
A dog adorer.

Holly Owen (9)
Ysgol Y Waun, Wrexham

Guinea Pig Kennings

An annoying squeaker,
A long scraper,
A furry figure,
A little biter,
A silent snoozer,
A mess maker.

Ewan Roberts (8)
Ysgol Y Waun, Wrexham

Bulldog Kennings

A gorilla guard,
A hard headbutter,
A nose breaker,
A tongue tugger,
A loud barker.

Ethan Gilbert (9)
Ysgol Y Waun, Wrexham

Nan

A money giver,
A bingo performer,
A cake baker,
A home admirer,
A sofa adorer.

Joe Evans (9)
Ysgol Y Waun, Wrexham

Rabbit Kennings

A speedy eater,
A slow drinker,
A loud leaper,
A self licker,
A steady jumper.

Jenabai Kassam (8)
Ysgol Y Waun, Wrexham

Butterflies Poems

A short liver,
A fast flyer,
A delicate creature,
A leaf adorer,
A wing spreader,
A beautiful glider,
A rainbow winger.

Paige Davenport (8)
Ysgol Y Waun, Wrexham

Kennings Horse

A fabulous jumper,
A lawn eater,
An aqua drinker,
A saddle wearer,
A speedy runner,
An amazing winner,
A shoe wearer.

Anna Jones (8)
Ysgol Y Waun, Wrexham

Pharmacist Kennings

An antibiotic sorter
A time watcher
A uniform wearer
A needle giver
A nocturnal worker.

Ryan Windust (8)
Ysgol Y Waun, Wrexham

My Referee Poem

A uniform wearer.
An argument breaker.
A whistle blower.
A card holder.
A free kick donor.
A penalty sorter.
A goal giver.

Sam Pearce (10)
Ysgol Y Waun, Wrexham

Holidaymaker

A phenomenal relaxer.
A splendid swimmer.
A coastline lover.
An arcade adorer.
A disco supporter.
A park player.
A good crabber.
A sunbather.

Miya Newell (9)
Ysgol Y Waun, Wrexham

Tennis Player Poem

An aqua drinker,
A towel user,
A record scorer,
A feisty competitor,
A ball striker.

Holly Nash (10)
Ysgol Y Waun, Wrexham

Doctor Kennings

A hard worker,
A computer worker,
A phone worker,
A tablet giver,
A get well helper.

Melissa Hughes (10)
Ysgol Y Waun, Wrexham

President Kennings

An announcement maker.
A debate sorter.
A country ruler.
A crime handler.
A referendum protector.
A statement manufacturer.

Mason Foulkes (9)
Ysgol Y Waun, Wrexham

Ruler Poem

A line drawer,
A measure helper,
A mm and cm measurer,
A work helper,
A number counter.

Bailey Roberts (9)
Ysgol Y Waun, Wrexham

A Victorian Poem

As hungry as an Aardvark.
As black as night.
As smelly as a skunk.
As damp as grass.
As scared as a bat.

As tasty as a sweet.
As cosy as a bed.
As green as grass.
As shiny as a star.
As tall as a giant.

As cold as ice.
As red as a rose.

Lewis Hurdsman (8)
Ysgol Y Waun, Wrexham

A Victorian Poem

As smelly as a skunk.
As wet as the rain.
As dark as the night sky.
As tall as the church.
As cold as a pile of ice.
As thin as a stick.

As dirty as a pig.
As lonely as an ugly duckling.
As scary as a mouse.
As rich as can be.
As tall as a tree.

As small as a beetle.
As warm as the sun.
As clean as soap.
As greedy as a pig.

Eryn Jones (8)
Ysgol Y Waun, Wrexham

A Victorian Poem

As cold as the South Pole.
As dirty as the world.
As red as lava.
As steep as Mount Everest.
As scared as a child in the factory.
As green as grass.

Ethan Hamblett (9)
Ysgol Y Waun, Wrexham

A Victorian Poem

As hungry as an aardvark.
As dirty as mud.
As smelly as a skunk.
As damp as grass.
As thin as a pike.

As tasty as toast.
As warm as a heater.
As lovely as a flower.
As shiny as gold.
As cosy as a bed.

As poor as Oliver Twist.
As rich as a king.
As poor as a pig.
As rich as my mum.
As poor as my dog.

Amber Nash (8)
Ysgol Y Waun, Wrexham

Singer Kennings

A world traveller,
A deadly dancer,
A pop entertainer,
A glam styler,
A music maker,
A show taker,
A move maker,
An overnight sensationer,
An award winner,
A memory maker,
A stage stopper,
A diva digger,
A fun X Factor.

Lucy Edwards (9)
Ysgol Y Waun, Wrexham

The Magic Box

I will put in the box . . .
The bitterness of the saddest tear,
The shine out of the diamond ring,
And the steaming heat out of the molten lava,
Fresh from the desolate Mount Vesuvius.

I will put in my box . . .
The deteriorated soul from the dead body.
The sound of a swooping bird, soaring through the sky,
Two croaks from the greenest frog; just in case one leaps out.

I will put in my box . . .
The cool breeze from the calm wind.
The feelings of joy and happiness that make you smile.
Sadness and despair that make you cry.
My box is made of diamond, gold and amethyst.
The lid is made of emerald, decorated with rainbows.
I will stand on my box as high as a mountain,
I will fly on my box
It will shine as it drops to the ground, faster than a rocket to mars.

My box will bring peace to the world as it brings in all of the deepest darkest deadliest secrets
Turning the world gold . . .

Ethan Gilbert (9)
Ysgol Y Waun, Wrexham

A Victorian Poem

As cosy as a pillow.
As warm as lava.
As rich as silk.
As lovely as gold.

Maisie Richards (8)
Ysgol Y Waun, Wrexham

YOUNG WRITERS INFORMATION

We hope you have enjoyed reading this book – and that you will continue to in the coming years.

If you're a young writer who enjoys reading and creative writing, or the parent of an enthusiastic poet or story writer, do visit our website www.youngwriters.co.uk. Here you will find free competitions, workshops and games, as well as recommended reads, a poetry glossary and our blog.

If you would like to order further copies of this book, or any of our other titles give us a call or visit **www.youngwriters.co.uk.**

Young Writers
Remus House
Coltsfoot Drive
Peterborough
PE2 9BF

(01733) 890066 / 898110
info@youngwriters.co.uk